the Far Side

by Gary Larson

Futura

Macdonald & Co

London & Sydney

A **Futura** Book

Copyright © 1982 by the Chronicle Publishing Company

First published in America in 1982 by Andrews and McMeel Inc.,
a Universal Press Syndicate Company, Kansas

This edition published in 1984 by Futura Publications,
a Division of Macdonald & Co (Publishers) Ltd
London & Sydney
Reprinted 1988, 1989, 1990

ISBN 0 7088 2624 5

Printed in Great Britain by
The Guernsey Press Company Limited,
Guernsey, Channel Islands

Futura Publications
A Division of
Macdonald & Co (Publishers) Ltd
Orbit House
1 New Fetter Lane
London EC4A 1AR

A Member of Maxwell Macmillan Pergamon Publishing Corporation

the Far Side

"Hold still, Carl! . . . Don't . . . move . . . an . . . inch!"

"Egad! . . . Sounds like the farmer's wife has really flipped out this time!"

"Now stay calm . . . Let's hear what they said to Bill."

"Well that's how it happened, Sylvia . . . I kissed this frog, he turns into a prince, we get married and wham! . . . I'm stuck at home with a bunch of pollywogs."

"So! . . . Out bob bob bobbing along again!"

"It's still hungry . . . and I've been stuffing worms into it all day."

"Thank God, Sylvia! We're alive!"

"So! . . . The little sweethearts were going to carve their initials on me, eh?"

"And I've only one thing to say about all these complaints I've been hearing about . . . venison!"

"Say, honey . . . didn't I meet you last night at the feeding-frenzy?"

"Okay, buddy. Then how 'bout the right arm?"

"Through the hoop, Bob! Through the hoop!"

"Something big's going down, sir . . . they're heading your way now!"

"Look at that! . . . Give me the good old days when a man carried a club and had a brain the size of a walnut."

"I've done it! The first real evidence of a
UFO! . . . And with my own camera, in my own
darkroom, and in my own . . ."

"Big Bob says he's getting tired of you saying he doesn't really exist."

"Yeah, Sylvia . . . my set too . . . and in the middle of 'Laverne and Shirley.' "

"Andrew, go out and get your grandfather . . . the squirrels have got him again."

"Thank God! . . . Those blasted crickets have finally stopped!"

"Okay . . . On the count of three everybody rattles."

"So then Carl says to me, 'Look . . . Let's invite over the new neighbors and check 'em out.'"

"One of the nicest evenings I've ever spent at the Wilson's . . . and then you had to go and do that on the rug!"

"The herring's nothin' . . . I'm going for the whole shmeer!"

"We've made it, Warren! . . . The moon!"

"I like it . . . I like it."

"Yoo-hoo! Oh, yoo-hoo! . . . I think I'm getting a blister."

"You imbecile! . . . We flew 12,000 miles for THIS?"

"Oh, brother! . . . Not hamsters again!"

"Well, we're back!"

"Andrew! So that's where you've been! And good
heavens! . . . There's my old hairbrush, too!"

"This is a test. For the next thirty seconds, this station will conduct a test of the emergency broadcast system . . ."

"Dear Henry: Where were you? We waited and waited but finally decided that . . ."

"So! . . . You STILL won't talk, eh?"

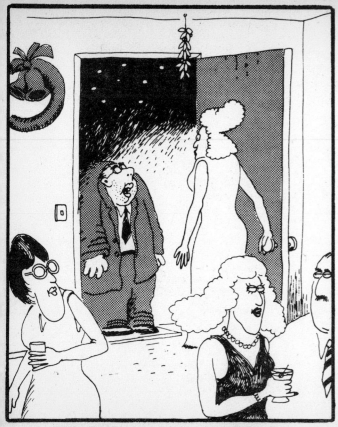

"Hello, I'm Clarence Jones from Bill's office and . . . Oh! Hey! Mistletoe!"

"This is just not effective . . . We need to get some chains."

"Ho! Just like every time, you'll get about 100 yards out before you start heading back."

"Wouldn't you know it! . . . There goes our market for those things!"

"You meathead! Now watch! . . . The rabbit goes through the hole, around the tree five or six times . . ."

"Excuse me, Harold, while I go slip into something more comfortable."

"We've got the murder weapon and the motive . . . now if we can just establish time-of-death."

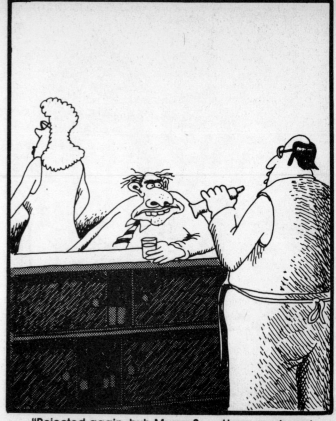

"Rejected again, huh Murray? . . . Have you heard about this new breath-freshening toothpaste?"

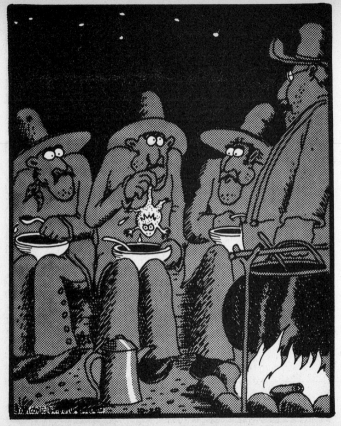

"Well I'll be! Eggbeater must have missed that one."

"Okay, Bob! Go! Go!"

"You idiots! . . . We'll never get that thing down the hole!"

"Look . . . You wanna try putting him back together again?"

"Gad, I hate walking through this place at night."

". . . and then the second group comes in — 'row, row, row your boat' . . ."

"Aphids! Aphids, Henry! . . . Aphids are loose in the garden!"

"Big one, Thag! . . . We caught biiiiig one!"

"Listen . . . this party's a drag. But later on, Floyd, Warren, and myself are going over to Farmer Brown's and slaughter some chickens."

"You're kidding! . . . I was struck twice by lightning too!"

"All units prepare to move in! . . . He's givin' him the duck now!"

"Still won't talk, huh? . . . Okay, no more Mr. Nice Guy."

"On the other hand, gentlemen, what if we gave a war and EVERYBODY came?"

"I could have guessed . . . my friends all warned me that this breed will sometimes turn on you."

"Go get 'em brother."

"See, Frank? Keep the light in their eyes and you can bag them without any trouble at all."

"An excellent specimen . . . symbol of beauty, innocence, and fragile life . . . hand me the jar of ether."

"Wait! Wait! . . . Cancel that, I guess it says 'helf.'"

"I'm afraid you've got cows, Mr. Farnsworth."

"Look. I just don't feel the relationship is working out."

"We're almost free, everyone! . . . I just felt the first drop of rain."

"Okay, Williams, we'll vote . . . how many here say the heart has four chambers?"

"I can't stand it . . . They're so CUTE when they sit like that."

"Don't encourage him, Sylvia."

"Anyone for a chorus of 'Happy Trails'?"

"I asked you a question, buddy . . . What's the square root of 5,248?"

"Early stages of math anxiety"

"For God's sake, kill the lights, Murray . . . He's back again!"

"Oh yeah? . . . And I suppose you got those suction marks at the meeting, too!"

"Hey! Look what Zog do!"

"Eraser fight!!"

"And next, for show-and-tell, Bobby Henderson says he has something he found on the beach last summer . . ."

"My word, Walter! . . . Sounded like a good-size bird just hit the window."

"So there he was — this big gorilla just laying there. And Jim says, 'Do you suppose it's dead or just asleep?'"

"I don't know where your father is tonight . . . No doubt out bangin' his head against some tree."

"Can I look now?"

"And so I've reached the conclusion, gentlemen, that the Wonker Wiener Company is riddled with incompetence."

"Vive la difference."

"We better do as he says, Thag . . . He's got the drop on us."

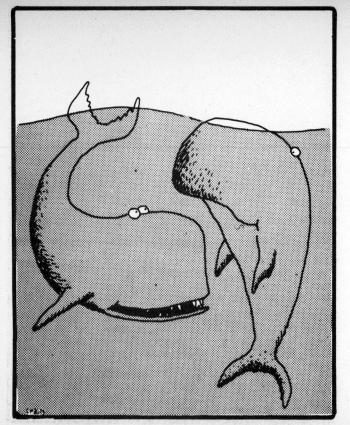

"I don't know . . . how many college students do you think you could eat at one time?"

"Well, I never thought about it before . . . but I suppose I'd let the kid go for about $1.99 a pound."

Near Gettysburg, 1863: A reflective moment.

"You heard me, Simmons! . . . You get that cursed
bugle fixed!"

"The revolution has been postponed . . . We've
discovered a leak."

"I told you guys to slow down and take it easy or something like this would happen."

"Well, so much for the unicorns . . . But, from now on, all carnivores will be confined to 'C' deck."

"Wouldn't you know it! Now the Hendersons have the bomb."

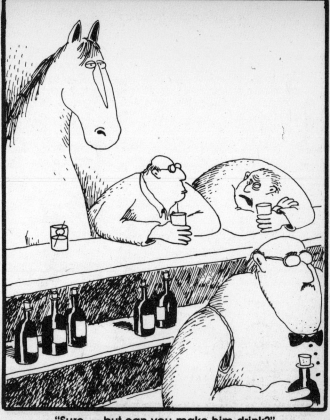

"Sure — but can you make him drink?"

"Knock, knock, knock . . . Ding dong, ding dong . . .
Anybody home? . . . Knock, knock, knock . . ."

"Just nibble at first . . . But when you hear them yell
'Piranha!' — go for it."

"My goodness, Harold . . . Now there goes one big mosquito."

"And remember! . . . I don't want to catch you bothering the fish!"

"With a little luck, they may revere us as gods."

"So! You admit that this is, indeed, your banjo the police found at the scene . . . But, you expect this jury to believe you were never in the kitchen with Dinah?"

"Are they gaining, Huxley?"

"Well, when it's my turn, I just hope I go quietly . . .
Without a lot of running around."

"You'll never get away with this!"

"It's no use . . . We've just got to get ourselves a real damsel."

"What? . . . You mean NO ONE brought the buns?"

"Gad! . . . Not *these* Indians again!"

"Hot oil! We need hot oil! . . . Forget the water balloons!"

"Hey, Durk! . . . New roommate, Durk! . . . New roommate! . . . Friend, Durk! . . . Friend! . . ."

"Skinny legs! . . . I got skinny legs!"

"Oh, wow! I can't believe this thing! . . . Does my voice really sound that funny?"

"Well I just think I've been putting up with this silly curse of yours long enough!"

"What a lovely home, Edna! . . . And look at the fresh newspaper, Stanley!"

"Why, yes . . . we do have two children who won't eat their vegetables."

"I got a bad feeling about this, Harriet."

"Something's wrong, here, Harriet . . . This is
starting to look less and less like Interstate 95."

"Quick, Agnes! Look! . . . There it is again!"

"I've got it, too, Omar . . . a strange feeling like
we've just been going in circles."

"Hey! I got one! I got one!"

"That settles it, Carl! . . . From now on, you're getting only decaffeinated coffee!"

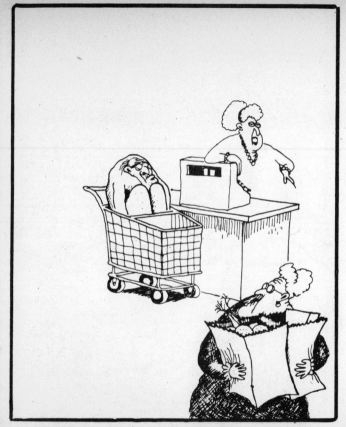

"Oh, Mrs. Oswald . . . you've forgotten something
again."

"So then this little sailor dude whips out a can of spinach, this crazy music starts playin', and . . . well, just look at this place."

"And another thing . . . I want you to be more assertive! I'm tired of everyone calling you Alexander the Pretty-Good!"

"Honey, the Merrimonts are here . . . They'd like to come down and see your ape-man project."

"It seems that agent 6373 has accomplished her mission."

"And now we're going to play she-loves-me, she-loves-me-not!"

"Agnes! It's that heavy, chewing sound again!"

"Don't be alarmed folks . . . He's completely
harmless unless something startles him."

"C'mon! Look at these fangs! . . . Look at these claws! . . . You think we're supposed to eat just honey and berries?"

"Go for it, Sidney! You've got it! You've got it! Good hands! Don't choke!"

"Counterclockwise, Red Eagle! Always counterclockwise!"

"For twelve perfect years I was a car-chaser. Pontiacs, Fords, Chryslers . . . I took them all on . . . and yesterday my stupid owner backs over me in the driveway."

I DON'T BRAKE

"Hey, c'mon now! . . . You two were MADE for each other!"

"You're embarrassing me, Warren."

"And, as you shall soon observe, we are quite proud of our test tube baby progress."

"Of course, living in an all-glass house has its disadvantages . . . but you should see the birds smack it."

"So! . . . You've been buzzing around the living room again!"

"And so, without further ado, here's the author of 'Mind over Matter' . . ."

"NOW we'll see if that dog can get in here!"

"Okay, Billy . . . Tide's coming in now . . . Dig me out, Billy . . . Billy, I don't want to get angry . . ."

"Remember, milk, eggs, loaf of bread . . . and pick up one of those No-Penguin-Strips."

"C'mon, Sylvia . . . where's your spirit of adventure?"

"I never got his name . . . but he sure cleaned up this town."

"This ain't gonna look good on our report, Leroy."

"For crying out loud! . . . You're ALWAYS hearing
something moving around downstairs!"

"Disgusting! . . . It's just a sort of heavy huffing and
puffing."

"Fair is fair, Larry . . . We're out of food, we drew straws — you lost."

"Okay, okay, okay . . . Everyone just calm down and we'll try this thing one more time."

Futura now offers an exciting range of quality fiction and non-fiction by both established and new authors.
All of the books in this series are available from good bookshops, or can be ordered from the following address:

Futura Books
Cash Sales Department
P.O. Box 11
Falmouth
Cornwall, TR10 9EN.

Please send cheque or postal order (no currency), and allow 60p for postage and packing for the first book plus 25p for the second book and 15p for each additional book ordered up to a maximum charge of £1.90 in U.K.

B.F.P.O. customers please allow 60p for the first book, 25p for the second book plus 15p per copy for the next 7 books, thereafter 9p per book.

Overseas customers, including Eire, please allow £1.25 for postage and packing for the first book, 75p for the second book and 28p for each subsequent title ordered.